The workplace is so often the primary context in which we engage our faith and, as such, it is crucial that Christians are missional in their work, examining the areas of brokenness they can push against—seeking to bring mercy and justice—in their respective fields. If every Christian considered how they can better love their neighbors on the margins, steward their power and be a restorative presence in their workplace, it would be nothing less than transformational. This course shows us how to do just that. It is an important aid to Christian discipleship and will help unleash congregants more fully to love people, places and systems to life.

TIMOTHY KELLER, chairman and cofounder, Redeemer City to City; author, *Every Good Endeavor: Connecting Your Work to God's Work*

The Missional Disciple is an immensely helpful resource for the church. It will help Christians connect Sunday morning to the rest of the week. It will show how the gospel gives rise to both mercy and justice. This workbook is holistic in its understanding of Jesus' work in our lives, drawing from the insights of communities of color and presenting material in creative, engaging and community formative ways. I encourage you to read this book with a small group of friends and expect to be transformed!

TISH HARRISON WARREN, Anglican priest, author, *Liturgy of the Ordinary* and *Prayer in the Night*

Faith and work theology is often quiet about applying passages such as Micah 6:8 to congregants' workplaces—whether one's workplace is at home, under a sink, or in an office building. Thankfully, Redeemer City to City has crafted this timely, accessible, practical and interactive course—intended for group study. Fellow travelers, who together explore this unchartered territory, will be emboldened to lead the way in applying Micah's moral injunctions to "act justly" and "love mercy" to their varied workplaces.

LUKE BOBO, chief program officer, Arrabon; former vice president, Networks, Made to Flourish; visiting professor, Contemporary Culture, Covenant Theological Seminary; author, *Race, Economics, and Apologetics; Worked Up: Navigating Calling After College;* and *Living Salty and Light-Filled Lives in the Workplace*

If you want to figure out how you can grow in mercy, love and justice in the workplace, this course is for you. With thoughtful speakers and case studies from a variety of industries, this curriculum is designed to help people across industries get very practical in the pursuit of mercy and justice through their work.

MICHAELA O'DONNELL, PhD, executive director, De Pree Center for Leadership, Fuller Seminary; author, *Make Work Matter: Your Guide to Meaningful Work in a Changing World*

In our individualistic culture, Christians, as people of integrity and righteousness, have often turned to God for help to endure the brokenness of our work lives. Far less often, however, do we consider and take responsibility for the goodness and justice of our companies and institutions. Perhaps, like the biblical character of Esther, we feel powerless. This course will equip us to be more missional, for perhaps God has put us in our positions "for such a time as this."

KATHERINE LEARY ALSDORF, founding director, Redeemer Presbyterian Church's Center for Faith & Work; global consultant and coach to churches seeking to equip their people for faith-full work in the world; assistant to Timothy Keller in the writing of *Every Good Endeavor: Connecting Your Work to God's Work*

This course provides a theologically robust, wise and challenging vision of how we can glorify God by pursuing mercy and justice in our daily work. If God's people can embrace what is taught in this course, I believe it will contribute to flourishing communities and bear witness to the God of mercy and justice. I plan on using this course with my congregation and cannot recommend it highly enough.

JIM MULLINS, lead pastor, Redemption Church, Tempe, Arizona; author, *The Symphony of Mission: Participating in God's Work in the World*

Our workplaces are often our primary places of engaging God's mission in the world. Doing so apart from a holistic, integrated theology of mercy and justice renders our pursuit of good work impoverished and incomplete. Investing six weeks in this learning experience will build new muscles for reimagining your workplace, and even your industry, through a fully orbed lens that can bring about redemption, restoration and a richer story of God's work in the world. But, be ready—you might never view work, justice and God's mission in quite the same way.

LISA SLAYTON, founder, Tamim Partners, LLC; director, CityGate

As the workplace continues to evolve, our view on work in relation to our faith must continue to grow as well. If we spend a major part of our waking hours working, then we must approach the subject in fuller ways. This material gives a more holistic approach to work, offering fresh thinking in a subject that is often in need of inspiration. This is a helpful guide, which will inspire you to approach your work more thoughtfully.

AARON BJERKE, pastor, The Well, New York City

The Missional Disciple

Pursuing Mercy & Justice at Work

A SIX-SESSION COURSE BY REDEEMER CITY TO CITY

REDEEMER
CITY to CITY

GLOBAL
FAITH & WORK
INITIATIVE
A MINISTRY OF REDEEMER CITY TO CITY

The Missional Disciple

Pursuing Mercy & Justice at Work

A SIX-SESSION COURSE BY REDEEMER CITY TO CITY

Redeemer City to City
57 W. 57th Street
4th Floor
New York
NY 10019
United States

www.redeemercitytocity.com

First published in 2022

ISBN 979-8-218-05595-0 (print)

ISBN 979-8-218-05992-7 (ebook)

*Authors: Kimberly Deckel, Lauren Gill, Charlie Meo, Dennae
Pierre, Missy Wallace*
Contributors: Abe Cho, Robert Guerrero, Susan Nacorda
General Editor: Lauren Gill
Videographers: Ben Stamper, Caroline Stucky
Cover Image: Recorder24/Shutterstock.com
*Inner Images: Monika7, gilzr, pixssa, Elizaveta, Mataz,
July Store/Shutterstock.com*
Cover design and interior design: Revo Creative
Publishing Manager: Anna Robinson

May the favor of the Lord our God rest on us;
establish the work of our hands for us—yes,
establish the work of our hands.

PSALM 90:17

He has shown you, O mortal, what is good.
*And what does the L*ORD *require of you? To act*
justly and to love mercy and to walk humbly with
your God.

MICAH 6:8

Contents

Course
Introduction

A Guide to the Holistic Course Experience

Living out our faith in the workplace can feel like a challenging endeavor. Whether we're comfortable viewing our kingdom calling in the context of work or we've never given it much thought, choosing to prayerfully consider God's will for our workplaces is an important journey to embark upon.

This course invites you to not only consider the importance of faith and work but also to integrate them with two key components of Christian mission: mercy and justice.

For many, this will be a new frontier. Assumptions will be challenged, systems and structures questioned, relationships reimagined and work re-narrated. You might enter this course believing a false dichotomy: embracing either a robust vision of faith and work *or* a compelling call to mercy and justice. But what would it look like for these two arenas to overlap?

Whether tending to beds in a hospital or starting a business, sitting at a call center or waiting tables in a restaurant, this course is for everyone seeking a biblically holistic paradigm for daily work. As we will discover, God's heart has always been for missional disciples to integrate mercy and justice at work. As you begin this journey, here are three key pointers for the adventure ahead.

POSTURE

Whenever we gain new insight and explore unfamiliar territory, our tendency is often to adopt a hurried pragmatism. If we take this approach, our learning usually remains shallow. It is therefore important to give the needed time and reflection to allow this content to transform the core of your being. Be wary of anxious activity as a counterfeit for prayerful participation in God's mission. The starting place for your journey is *posture*. Christians have been given many important identities as disciples of Jesus, yet one of the foundational identities is that of a learner. It's the very meaning of the word *disciple* (*mathetes*). Like an apprentice in the craftsman's workshop, allow your posture to be one of deep listening as you follow closely behind the skilled practitioners and theologians leading you in this course. It is this kind of posture that creates hearts of curiosity and an openness to the surprising work the Holy Spirit wants to do in and through Christians in every industry.

PEOPLE

The first rule of journeying into unexplored territory is to never go alone. It's impossible to integrate mercy and justice at work as a lone traveler. This course is designed to partner with fellow missional disciples, discerning together God's direction and vision for your work. The learning will not only come through the helpful videos that form part of this course but also through God's image-bearers, the *people* who sit next to you each week during community discussion. Don't overlook the group of people accompanying you the next six weeks. We need community to learn from people who are not like ourselves, to encourage vulnerability, to help us see our blind spots and to support us on this journey.

IMPLEMENTATION

A troubling trend of discipleship in the West is a fixation on ideas devoid of any real practice or implementation. It's the equivalent of an expeditionist who draws up the maps, gathers the tools and secures the funding yet never leaves the comfort of his or her warm living room. In the context of deep reflection, the vision of this course is to get your hands dirty in the messy and beautiful practice of executing mercy and justice through your work. Throughout this course there will be small invitations to see ideals become actualized. Prioritize *implementation* of the practices each week as you journey together.

How To Use This Course

Whether you're the group leader or simply a participant, below are some guidelines on how to get the best out of this course.

WORKBOOK

The starting place for this course is this workbook. For each of the six weeks, you will be given an introduction, videos, objectives, assignments, discussion questions, prayer prompts and a practice for the following week. As you journey, let the workbook guide you through the direction of each lesson. However, this course is insufficient without viewing the videos, which are the main method of teaching.

VIDEOS

This course is designed around short videos presented by leading practitioners who are integrating mercy and justice at work. Each week, there will be two to three short videos to watch. You can either watch these videos when you gather for group discussion, or you can watch them beforehand and come ready to dialogue together.

To access the videos, you can scan the QR codes in each lesson with your phone. Alternatively, you can view all the videos at globalfaithandwork.com/missionaldisciplevideos.

COMMUNITY DISCUSSION

The majority of your group time will be spent discussing the core themes and ideas presented that week. Use the questions in this workbook to guide and lead the discussion. The questions are not intended as an end point but rather as a starting place for what the Holy Spirit might want to do in your workplace.

PRACTICES

Each week you will be sent out with a simple practice related to the theme of the lesson. This is where the learning becomes tangible. Encourage others in your group to engage with the practice each week, as it is crucial to the learning process. The group discussion section for weeks two to six will create space for reflection on the previous week's practice. Use this time to share how the practice went, to confess any failure and to encourage one another in the meaningful work in which you are participating.

PRAYER PROMPTS

Finally, each week you will be given prayer prompts that can be used to guide your group in a time of prayer before you close your session together, as well as throughout the week. Prayer is core to this entire journey because, ultimately, it is God himself who has called you to the way of mercy and justice, and he will be your Helper, Counselor and Encourager along the path.

Let's Begin

To begin, please watch the "Course Introduction" video with Lauren Gill. You can scan the QR code or visit globalfaithandwork.com/missionaldisciplevideos to access this short welcome video. Once you've watched this video, please continue straight to Lesson 1.

Course
Introduction

A Holistic View of Restoration Through Work

Introduction

Imagine walking out of your front door and asking the first ten people you see this question: "How would you define the meaning and purpose of work?" What kinds of answers do you think you would receive?

If you live in a large city, with people from diverse backgrounds, you are likely to hear ten very different responses. Why is this? Because our understanding of work is derived from the story in which we are living. Regardless of background or location, humans are thoroughly story-shaped creatures. In *After Virtue*, philosopher Alasdair MacIntyre says, "I can only answer the question 'What am I to do?' if I can answer the prior question of 'Of what story or stories do I find myself a part of?'"*

The vision of this course is for everyday Christians to recognize mercy and justice as one of the core dimensions of our work. However, as MacIntyre notes, before we get to "What am I to do?" we need to start with "What story am I a part of?" Sadly, we often fail to realize how the cultural stories of our day have deliberately and deceptively shaped our vision of work. It's time for some healthy re-narration.

* Alasdair MacIntyre, *After Virtue: A Study in Moral Theory* (Notre Dame: University of Notre Dame Press, 2007 [3rd ed]), 216.

This week, Dennae Pierre will unpack a vision of work and its intersection with justice and mercy from the biblical narrative, using six simple symbols.**

⌄ **Creation**   ⊗ **Rebellion**   ⊘ **Promise**   ⊕ **Redemption**   ⊘ **Church**   ⌄ **Restoration**

Dennae will trace how work and its intersection with justice is an integral plotline of God's unfolding mission. The beauty of the biblical story is that it not only casts a holistic vision of work but also calls Christians to embody a particular identity: a restorative presence. As you take up your role in God's unfolding drama, you become a person who can create, redeem and heal, right where you are in your everyday life.

Lastly, you will watch a case study from Teena Dare, to give you a glimpse of what a story-formed vision of work and justice looks like in an overlooked area of her industry.

Don't move too quickly through this first lesson—it is the foundation and framework for everything to follow.

** Biblical Narrative symbols created by Chris Gonzalez and Kevin Platt, Missio Dei Communities, 2008.

OBJECTIVES

- Share a biblical-shaped vision of work, using the six symbols.

- Identify the other stories that have shaped your vision of work.

- Imagine what a restorative presence could look like in your workplace.

Assignments

- Watch: "**Work within the Biblical Narrative**" video with Dennae Pierre.

- Watch: "**Restorative Leadership**" video with Dennae Pierre.

- Watch "**Case Study: Hospitality**" video with Teena Dare.

- Practice: Naming the Other Stories.

(Videos can be accessed by scanning the QR codes or by visiting globalfaithandwork.com/missionaldisciplevideos.)

Work within the Biblical Narrative

Restorative Leadership

Case Study: Hospitality

COMMUNITY DISCUSSION

- As you heard Dennae walk through a vision of work through the six-act biblical narrative, what was a new insight for you?

- On a piece of paper, whiteboard or digital screen, draw the six symbols of the story Dennae outlined. Once you have drawn the symbols, get into groups of three. In your group, each person will have three minutes to tell the biblical narrative from creation to restoration, emphasizing work as a core part of the plotline. As each person shares, make sure to encourage them in the insights they uniquely highlighted. For the group as a whole, answer the following questions: Which parts of the story were easiest to tell? Which parts were hardest?

- Being a restorative presence in your work includes three primary practices:

  1 Being rooted in Christ.

  2 Being a cultivator of community.

  3 Being an advocate of justice in systems and structures.

  In which of these practices do you feel strongest? In which do you feel weakest?

- Consider Teena's case study in light of the restorative leadership framework. In an industry where many might consider a waitress as having little power, how did Teena steward her power for those on the margins? Can you brainstorm ways you can steward your power well in the work God has given you?

PRACTICE: Naming the Other Stories

The practice this week is to grow in your ability to name the other stories that have shaped your vision of work. Consider the following three primary influences:

1 Your family of origin: *How did your family talk about work?*

2 Your cultural setting: *What story does your cultural context tell of work?*

3 Your current work/industry: *How do your coworkers and industry view the purpose of work?*

If helpful, you can use your own symbols to tell the stories of these three primary shaping environments. Is there any overlap or disagreement between your family, culture and current industry's story of work and the biblical story? As you think about these other stories, do they celebrate people embodying a restorative presence, like Dennae outlined? If not, who do these other stories celebrate as the pinnacle of success or meaningful work? What has been revealed to you through this exercise? Be ready to share these insights with your group the next time you meet.

PRAYER PROMPTS

- Pray that the biblical narrative would be the story through which you view all other stories, including the story and purpose of your work.

- Ask God to help you identify and address ways that other stories have shaped the way you think about and approach your work more than the biblical narrative.

- Pray that God would help you and each member of your group to become a restorative presence in your workplace.

Notes

Defining
Biblical Justice

Introduction

One of the most complicated, challenging and sometimes polarizing subjects is the issue of justice.

What is it? What does it look like? How might one go about embodying justice personally and corporately?

In recent years, many Christians have been navigating the multi-layered conversations surrounding justice, particularly asking the key question: *What relationship, if any, is there between justice and the gospel?*

In week one, we saw how work is a vital aspect of the biblical story, from creation to restoration. This week, we will look at how justice is not only central to the story but is also at the very heart of the character of God. In fact, there is an intimate relationship between justice and the gospel seen throughout the pages of Scripture.

In this week's first video, Kimberly Deckel is going to unpack a biblical vision of justice. She will uncover the two primary forms of justice in Scripture: retributive and reparative. With these forms in mind, she will walk us through the four key facets of biblical justice: generosity, equality, advocacy and responsibility. Many of our justice conversations tend to focus on one of these forms or aspects at the expense of the others, yet the Bible holds all of them beautifully in tension.

In the second video, Missy Wallace unpacks how these forms and aspects of justice relate to both persons and systems. She outlines a useful quadrant, which highlights views of both personal brokenness as well as broken systems, and helps us see how our understanding of brokenness in the world affects how we allow the gospel to be unleashed in our work.

Depending on your tradition or background, there is a high likelihood that you will gravitate toward either "saving" people or "fixing" systems when you attempt to embody

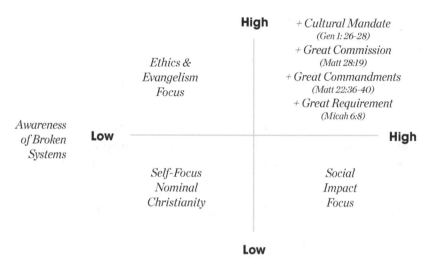

High

Ethics &
Evangelism
Focus

+ *Cultural Mandate*
  (Gen 1: 26-28)
+ *Great Commission*
  (Matt 28:19)
+ *Great Commandments*
  (Matt 22:36-40)
+ *Great Requirement*
  (Micah 6:8)

Awareness
of Broken
Systems

Low   **High**

Self-Focus
Nominal
Christianity

Social
Impact
Focus

Low

Awareness of Personal Brokenness

justice in your place of employment or industry. Missy will challenge you to not settle for an either/or vision of personal or systemic brokenness but rather to embrace a biblical understanding of both/and. Through this comprehensive understanding of brokenness, we can unleash the cultural mandate (create flourishing in the world: Genesis 1:26–28), the Great Commission (go out and make disciples: Matthew 28:18–19), the Great Commandments (love God and love others: Matthew 22:36–40) and the Micah requirement (do justice and love mercy: Micah 6:8) all throughout our day-to-day work. Every square inch of God's creation has been marred by sin and injustice, but in the already-but-not-yet reality—between Christ's ascension and second coming—every square inch is being redeemed and restored. *

You might be thinking all this sounds great in theory, but what does it mean in the daily realities of your workplace and industry? The last video for this week is a case study with Katrina Miles. As you listen to Katrina, notice how she embodies through her work the four biblical aspects of justice: generosity, equality, advocacy and responsibility.

* "Square inch" language comes from Abraham Kuyper's 1880 speech at Free University, Amsterdam, when he said, "There is not a square inch in the whole domain of human existence over which Christ, who is Sovereign over all, does not cry: 'Mine!'"

OBJECTIVES

- Identify a biblical vision of justice in light of the many competing visions of justice in culture.

- Explore the four dimensions of justice (generosity, equality, advocacy and responsibility) as they relate to your current practices in your work and industry.

- Reflect on how your tradition or background has shaped your understanding of justice, using the "Faith & Work Amidst Brokenness" quadrant.

Assignments

- Watch: "*What Does Biblical Justice Look Like?*" video with Kimberly Deckel.

- Watch: "*Faith & Work Amidst Brokenness*" video with Missy Wallace.

- Watch: "*Case Study: Commercial Arts*" video with Katrina Miles.

- Practice: GEAR in Your Work.

(Videos can be accessed by scanning the QR codes or by visiting globalfaithandwork.com/missionaldisciplevideos.)

What Does Biblical Justice Look Like?

Faith & Work Amidst Brokenness

Case Study: Commercial Arts

COMMUNITY DISCUSSION

- Reflect on your practice from last week: "Naming the Other Stories." Have two to three people in your group share about what they learned in uncovering their family, cultural and industry's vision of work.

- In the first video, Kimberly highlights that justice is found in the very character of God. Can you think of particular moments from creation to restoration where you see God acting justly, using either retribution or reparation? Why does it matter that God practices both forms?

- Process as a group how you think Jesus' death on the cross and resurrection fit into God's retributive and reparative vision of justice.

- Which of the four facets of justice (generosity, equality, advocacy and responsibility) do you tend to focus on? Which one do you tend to neglect?

- Consider the "Faith & Work Amidst Brokenness" quadrant Missy shared. From your tradition and background, have you tended to emphasize one or other of the personal or systemic dimensions of justice and sin? Can you think of someone from a different background who emphasizes the opposite dimension? What blind spots could they be revealing to you in your own life?

- Discuss with your group one facet of justice (generosity, equality, advocacy or responsibility) that is evident in Katrina's work in the commercial arts field.

PRACTICE: GEAR in Your Work

Your practice this week involves identifying a person or group of people in your work or industry who seem to be treated unfairly. You could also consider an industry you often intersect with in your work. With this person or group in mind, use the GEAR acronym to recognize where both justice and injustice are currently taking place.

- **GENEROSITY**: As you go about your work this week, observe who in your workplace or industry regularly practices generosity toward others. If there isn't anyone, consider what generosity might tangibly look like in your sphere of work.

- **EQUALITY**: Are there areas in your workplace or industry where an individual or group are not being treated as image-bearers of God?

- **ADVOCACY**: Is there an issue in your workplace or industry where you could be advocating for the poor, weak or powerless (or even a group that has less agency than you) in a way that reflects God's character?

- **RESPONSIBILITY**: With your current standing and power in your company/industry, where could you seek justice and repair, and work toward restoration?

As you respond to these questions during this coming week, make notes on your reflections and answers. Come prepared to discuss your insights with your group the next time you gather. As you think about the person or group treated unfairly, write down some of the ways you are praying specifically for them and your workplace.

PRAYER PROMPTS

- Pray that God would give you a humble and learning posture as you seek to understand a biblical view of justice amidst the many competing definitions in the world.

- Pray that God would help you learn how to practice generosity, equality, advocacy and responsibility in and through your day-to-day work.

- Pray that God would help you to learn about and address both personal brokenness and the broken systems in your workplace and industry.

Notes

Heart

The Inner Life of a Leader

Introduction

For the past two weeks, you have been given an aerial view of God's creation-wide vision of work and his heart for justice.

All our work has been broken by sin, yet by the power of Jesus, all of it can become an opportunity to embody a restorative presence. In a world quick to divide with competing visions of justice, God's story holds both personal and systemic justice together. The gospel is for individuals, organizations, institutions, systems and even nature itself. The gospel implores us to love people, places and things in ways that bring renewal to his creation.

Now that the biblical foundation has been laid and the framework outlined, you are on the precipice of becoming people who integrate faith and work with mercy and justice in your jobs and industries. So where to start? It begins with your heart.

As you begin to engage with areas of injustice in your work, various emotions may naturally arise. You may experience discomfort as you bear witness to the suffering of others, as you begin to explore the implications of certain injustices, or as you push against brokenness and practice mercy and justice. In every moment of discomfort, you may be tempted to look away or come up with reasons why you shouldn't get involved. It is in these precise moments that it's important to take time to examine your heart. Invite the Holy Spirit to reveal why these feelings are arising and to remind you of God's purposes.

Often, the reason we do not live into our identity as a restorative presence is simply because our hearts desire other things more than we desire God. Scripture refers to these things as idols. In your day-to-day work, idols can prevent you from centering and serving those on the margins. This week, Abe Cho will take you on a journey of exploring how idols, which began as good aspects of God's creation (comfort, approval, control and power), can become functional saviors, taking us away from the purposes of Christ.

+ Comfort
+ Approval
+ Control
+ Power

As Abe says in the video, the work of justice and mercy must flow from a place of gospel joy, which will give us the stamina and endurance to be a restorative presence over a long period of time. Yet to become this kind of person, we must allow Christ into the places of blindness and sickness in our soul. The practice for this week will involve taking an inventory of the idols that prevent you from embodying justice in your sphere. As you engage with this, hear this good news: Jesus comes not with a knife to harm you but with a scalpel to heal you. Will you allow him to do this deep work in you so that he might do powerful work through you?

After watching Abe's video on idolatry, you will watch Ben Stamper discuss his experience in the film industry. As you listen to Ben share the story of a young art student he worked with, notice how he identifies some of the brokenness of his industry and how a rich relationship with Christ allows him to operate differently.

- Identify and expose the heart idols that prevent you from being a restorative presence and working toward justice in and through your workplace.

- Contextualize how you can apply the gospel to your idols in ways that draw you into a deeper relationship with Christ.

- Grow in awareness of how the gospel can minister to your brokenness and how that can ultimately release you to more sustainable practices of justice and mercy in your industry.

Assignments

- Watch: *"Idolatry & Pursuing Those on the Margins"* video with Abe Cho.

- Watch: *"Case Study: Filmmaking"* video with Ben Stamper.

- Practice: Heart Inventory.

(Videos can be accessed by scanning the QR codes or by visiting globalfaithandwork.com/missionaldisciplevideos.)

*Idolatry &
Pursuing Those
on the Margins*

*Case Study:
Filmmaking*

COMMUNITY DISCUSSION

- Reflect on your practice from Lesson 2: "GEAR In Your Work." What did you discover from your experiences this past week that you can share with your group? What prayers did you find yourself praying? Did you learn anything unexpectedly?

- After reflecting on last week's practice, take a few moments together in silence, and process this question in your heart: *Which of the idols that Abe shared prevents me from being a restorative presence?* For those who are willing to share, take some time to name these idols to one another after the silence ends.

- As different personal idols are exposed and confessed, spend some time as a group, speaking the gospel to one another with this idol in mind. As you consider the life of Jesus, where do you see him dismantling this idol and inviting you into a different way of working and living?

- Have each person identify the person or group within their workplace or industry who has the least amount of power. With that person/group in mind, reflect collectively on which idols are at play that create and perpetuate their marginalization. Are there ways you have allowed these idols to prevent you from initiating love toward those with less power or agency in your industry or field?

- What are the indicators in your own heart that you are being motivated by gospel joy and the Holy Spirit in your pursuit of justice?

- In what ways does Ben's description of being a restorative presence at work resonate with you?

PRACTICE: Heart Inventory

This week's practice will dig in more deeply to the conversation you had with your group. Think about this question you answered in your community discussion this week: *Which of the idols shared prevents me from being a restorative presence?*

PART 1: PRAYER

Start your time by praying this Scripture slowly:

> *Search me, God, and know*
> *my heart;*
> *test me and know my*
> *anxious thoughts.*
> *See if there is any offensive*
> *way in me,*
> *and lead me in the way*
> *everlasting.*
>
> PSALM 139:23–24

Now, prayerfully ask God to search you and reveal any area that might be keeping you from being a restorative presence in your field of work. Spend some time in silence, reflecting on this Scripture.

PART 2: REFLECTION

As you sit with God, consider each of these questions, which are meant to serve as reflections on each of the four idols: comfort, approval, control and power.

- Are there ways your need for *comfort* keeps you from moving toward those who are different or on the margins, or from using your finances or resources in a way that is generous toward others?

- Are there ways you have not advocated for a person or group because you fear it may not meet with the *approval* of others?

- Are there ways in which a desire for *control* has kept you from including others who have a different perspective than yourself?

- Are there ways in which a scarcity mindset has made you fearful of giving *power* and agency to others, in case it means a loss of your own influence?

- Are there other ways these idols keep you from initiating love toward those on the margins?

JOURNAL YOUR RESPONSES HERE:

PART 3: WHAT DOES THE GOSPEL SAY?

Once you have identified an idol, ask the question, *What does the gospel say about this issue?* When our idols are revealed, it shows us where our hearts are us-centered rather than God-centered. It reveals to us the ways our desires are not aligned with what brings glory to Christ.

With your idol in mind, consider these questions:

- When that idol arises, in whom and in what are you trusting?

- What are you doubting about God's nature and promises that has you placing your trust in this idol? What are you fearing?

- What does Scripture have to say about this misplaced trust or fear?

- How would you respond differently in this area if you were trusting in Christ and his gracious provision in your life?

JOURNAL YOUR RESPONSES HERE:

PART 4: MOVING TOWARD CHRIST

Go back into a time of prayer. Spend some time in repentance, confessing how your worship of this particular idol has kept you from loving others. Thank God for what he has revealed about your brokenness, recognizing it is an opportunity for a deeper experience of his grace. Meditate on the truth that Christ died for this sin, and all our sins, and how he voluntarily gave up comfort, approval, control and power on the cross out of love for you.

Commit to allowing the love of Christ to shape your identity and desires. As you do this, you are inviting his love to renew and restore your heart in ways that allow you to do the work of mercy and justice over your lifetime through the power of the Holy Spirit.

PART 5: MOVING TOWARD A FRIEND

As you complete the practice this week, reach out to someone in your group to share what God graciously revealed to you during your time. It could look like getting together for coffee or calling someone on the phone.

PRAYER PROMPTS

- Pray that God would help you identify and repent of idols that deter you from caring for and serving those on the margins in your workplace.

- Praise God that Jesus gave up comfort, approval, control and power on the cross out of his sacrificial love for us so that we might have a new identity in him.

- Pray that God would help you take one step to confront or dethrone one of your idols in your work this week.

Notes

Community

*Loving Your Neighbor
Through Your Work*

Introduction

Last week, you reflected on how human hearts and entire industries have been shaped by powerful idols that prevent justice and flourishing from happening for both you and your coworkers.

The gospel is not only powerful for your own personal transformation but also for social transformation. The gospel transforms hearts and communities, including the communities at your work. This week, you will explore how to love your neighbor in and through your work.

As Jesus moved from heaven into the neighborhood of earth, his mission was to not only see individuals redeemed but also to create a people for himself, a beloved community. The beauty of the gospel is most fully on display through a community of God's image-bearers. To help you grasp a picture of this kind of community, in this week's first video, Kimberly Deckel outlines the principles of what Martin Luther King Jr. and others refer to as "beloved community." Kimberly organizes these principles into four pillars:

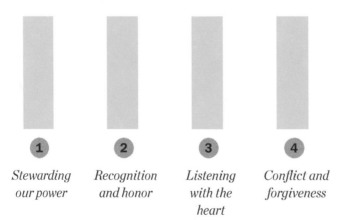

1. *Stewarding our power*
2. *Recognition and honor*
3. *Listening with the heart*
4. *Conflict and forgiveness*

These four aspects practiced together in your workplace create environments for coworkers and industries to experience a "thin space," where heaven and earth meet. It's tempting to see these notions of beloved community through a romanticized lens, but in reality, forming this kind of community requires you to get your hands dirty and will involve creating relationships with people who don't look or think the same as you. To do this work, you will need to create proximity to those who are excluded, overlooked or pushed to the margins of your work or industry.

In the second video, Robert Guerrero will challenge you to remember that at the core of Jesus' ministry and at the heart of the Great Commission is a call to spend time on the margins of the world. Why? Because it's the margins that Jesus chose to make the focus of his ministry and where he took up residence. As the margins are centered, a new kind of economy is born, where everyone has something to offer and contribute—not just those with the most resources or power. There are untapped gifts and potential in every sphere that through proximity can be revealed and celebrated by all. As pastor Bryan Loritts says, "Distance breeds suspicion. Proximity breeds empathy."*

You will end your time this week watching a case study video by Lisa Hertzog, who works in the educational field of New York City. As you listen to Lisa share her experience, take note of how she has done the hard work of creating proximity to students and families who are different from her so that she might uncover their hidden potential and gifts in the classroom. Also notice how examining her own heart led her to relate to her coworkers in a way that was more loving and collaborative.

OBJECTIVES

- Consider what might change in your workplace if the four pillars of beloved community were present.

- Evaluate your personal proximity to the margins of your workplace or industry.

- Pursue real friendship with an unlikely person in your workplace or industry.

Assignments

- Watch: "*Principles of Beloved Community*" video with Kimberly Deckel.

- Watch: "*Proximity to those on the Margins*" video with Robert Guerrero.

- Watch: "*Case Study: Education*" video with Liza Hertzog.

- Practice: Relational Inventory.

(Videos can be accessed by scanning the QR codes or by visiting globalfaithandwork.com/missionaldisciplevideos.)

Principles of Beloved Community

Proximity to those on the Margins

Case Study: Education

COMMUNITY DISCUSSION

- Consider your practice from last week: "Heart Inventory." What idols were revealed during your time of reflection and silence? Did you get a chance to share your discoveries with someone from your group and explore how the gospel is good news to each of the idols that were exposed? How was that experience for you? In what ways have you gained freedom to live differently?

- Which of the four pillars of beloved community (stewarding our power, recognition and honor, listening with the heart, conflict and forgiveness) are you strongest at embodying? Weakest?

- Which of the beloved community principles are already embodied in your workplace? Give a specific example. Can you imagine introducing a new beloved community principle into your workplace (your team, your staff, etc.)?

- Was there anything Robert shared that challenged your paradigm of what it means to follow Jesus?

- If Jesus was physically present in your city today, where would he be, and with whom would he be spending his time? How about in your industry or at your workplace?

- Consider Lisa's vulnerable example about how Jesus revealed to her ways she could be more loving toward her coworkers. Are there people in your workplace (customers, coworkers, clients or competitors) whom God may be calling you to treat differently?

PRACTICE: Relationship Inventory

You learned that proximity to those on the margins is essential to integrating a vision of faith and work with mercy and justice. Therefore, this week you are going to do a relationship inventory. This inventory is designed to not only help you identify relational dynamics at play but to also step toward others in relationship. This week, reflect on the following questions:

- Who in your workplace or industry holds the most power? Who holds the least?

- Do you have relationships with those who are often overlooked or undervalued in your workplace or with those who are directly affected by your work, such as your customers or those in your supply chain?

- What would it look like to create genuine relationships, where there is mutual giving and receiving?

- What could you do this week to pursue real friendship with an unlikely person in your workplace or industry?

Text someone from your group and share your plans of how you intend to begin building a genuine friendship with an unlikely person in your workplace or industry. Remember that those on the margins of your industry or workplace are not projects to be accomplished or problems to solve. Rather, they have good gifts to bring and deep insights to offer. What would it look like to create space for these gifts and insights to be seen by all?

PRAYER PROMPTS

- Pray that God would help you love your neighbors well, in and through your work, by stewarding your power; recognizing and honoring the image of God in every coworker or client; listening with your heart; and practicing conflict and forgiveness well.

- Pray that God would help you build authentic friendships of mutual giving and receiving with people on the margins.

Notes

05

World

*Work that Restores—
Pushing Against
Brokenness in Your Field*

Introduction

As Christians, we are sometimes tempted to adopt a dualistic mindset, viewing aspects of the world as either entirely good or entirely bad.

This is often evident in our approach to work, which we tend to see through an "either-or" lens: either our work, or a particular industry, is good and contributes to human flourishing or it is utterly broken and contributes to personal and systemic sinfulness. But what if we could view our work through a different lens, through the storyline of the Bible?

This week, Abe Cho is going to introduce you to a three-fold lens through which to view your industry and work.

Ⓒ **Creation**
Ⓕ **Fall**
Ⓡ **Redemption**

First, Abe will invite you to see your industry through a *creation* lens, recognizing the inherent goodness and dignity of your work and how it contributes to human flourishing. As C. S. Lewis says, "Badness is only spoiled goodness."* We can find glimpses of creational goodness in almost every sphere of human work, regardless of how spoiled it has become.

---

* C. S. Lewis, *Mere Christianity* (New York: HarperCollins, 2009), 44.

Second, Abe will invite you to use the lens of the *fall*. How has your work and industry been distorted and marred by the effects of sin—personally, communally and structurally?

Lastly, you will look at your work and industry through a *redemptive* lens. Professor and author Al Wolters says, "God doesn't make junk, and he doesn't junk what he's made."** God does not abandon his creation. He is on a mission in your field and in all of creation to redeem and restore all things. What would it look like to develop a kingdom imagination to see Jesus interrupting the brokenness of your industry and to identify where Jesus is sowing the seeds of new creation in your midst? As composer Isaac Watts wrote in his 1719 hymn "Joy to The World," Jesus' redemption stretches as "far as the curse is found." This redemption includes your field of work.

Let's explore this together.

** Albert M. Wolters, *Creation Regained: Biblical Basics for a Reformational Worldview* (Grand Rapids, MI: W.B. Eerdmans Pub. Co, 1985), 49.

OBJECTIVES

- Develop a three-fold lens (creation-fall-redemption) through which to understand the nature of your work and industry.

- Understand the "structure and direction" framework, outlined by Al Wolters in *Creation Regained.* ***

- Winsomely articulate to Christian and non-Christian coworkers this new lens and vision for your work.

Assignments

- Watch: "***Creational Goodness and Brokenness in a Field***" video with Abe Cho.

- Watch: "***Case Study: Finance***" video with Regina Green.

- Practice: Reimagine/Share/Re-Narrate for a Friend or Colleague this New Vision for Your Work.

(Videos can be accessed by scanning the QR codes or by visiting globalfaithandwork.com/missionaldisciplevideos.)

Creational Goodness and Brokenness in a Field

Case Study: Finance

*** The three-fold lens of "Creation-Fall-Redemption" and the idea of "structure and direction" used by Abe Cho in the video and in this workbook are based on the original ideas and insights of Al Wolters in his book *Creation Regained*, 87-114.

COMMUNITY DISCUSSION

- Reflect on your practice from last week: "Relational Inventory." What insights did you gain? What new relationships are you desiring to cultivate with those on the margins of your industry or workplace? What gifts did you uncover among those potentially overlooked in your field?

- As you think about the three lenses (creation-fall-redemption), which one is most overt in your work or industry? Which one is least overt, and why?

- As a group, have each participant share about their workplace or industry in this way:

  - Where do you see creational goodness and intent in your workplace or industry? What attributes or characteristics of God are represented in the industry?

  - Where do you experience the distortion and brokenness of the fall in your workplace or industry?

  - Where do you get a glimpse of Jesus' restorative kingdom in your workplace or industry? Imagine together what your industry or business would look like if God's kingdom were to fully break in.

- As you think about your coworkers, which lenses do you feel they are using to view their workplace or industry?

- Is there a way for you to explain the truths of creational goodness and structural brokenness using secular language?

- How does Regina's case study show how the creation-fall-redemption lens manifests in her industry?

PRACTICE : Reimagine/Share/ Re-Narrate for a Friend or Colleague This New Vision for Your Work

The practice this week is to find an opportunity to winsomely articulate a creation-fall-redemption lens of your work to a coworker. Avoid using explicitly "Christian" words but rather identify where your industry's values and practices might already give a glimpse of the creation-fall-redemption lens. Spend some time with your group, brainstorming what this could look like. Whether it's reframing the vision of your company in a team meeting, talking with a coworker while you complete a menial task or sending someone an encouraging note through this lens, think about how you can re-narrate how Jesus might view the best version of their industry.

As an example, take a look at the table below, which helps us consider how the work of janitors and custodians can be viewed through the creation-fall-redemption framework.

INDUSTRY: CLEANING SERVICES (JANITORS/CUSTODIANS)

CREATION

Humanity's mandate in Genesis was to steward God's good creation so that all might flourish. The role of the janitor/ custodian is to steward a space for others to use where they can flourish. They do this by mopping floors, tending to trash, replenishing toilet paper in bathrooms, solving problems or fixing broken things.

FALL

The creation God made has been marred by sin, sickness and disease. Within this industry, janitors are often given the task of responding to the consequences of sin: destroyed property, spills and stains, overflowing toilets, pests, and building damages. As employees, they are often overlooked, working invisible hours to maintain an environment with little to no recognition.

REDEMPTION

Jesus was the Great Janitor/ Custodian who took on the sicknesses and diseases of the world, cleansing hearts, bodies and spaces. Janitors/ custodians do the hidden work of disinfecting spaces, preventing the spread of millions of germs and diseases. They keep walkways and floors clear of debris and spills so that others might flourish as they walk through them.

PRAYER PROMPTS

- Pray that God would help you to see your workplace and industry through the three-fold lens of creation-fall-redemption so that you might join him in his restorative work.

- Pray that God would give you an opportunity to help point your non-Christian coworkers to the gospel by sharing a redemptive view of their work or your workplace.

- Pray for your workplace or industry, that God would bring his restoration and renewal.

Notes

06

The Path Forward

Introduction

You have made it to the final week of this course!

Over the weeks, you have covered a lot of ground, exploring how mercy and justice can take root in your work to see persons and systems flourish under God's care. For a moment, let's recap just how far you have come.

In week one, you reimagined your vision of work through the biblical narrative and what it might look like to embody a restorative presence in light of God's unfolding story.

In week two, you explored how the complex theme of justice and mercy is at the very heart of God's character and desire for the world. You were given the helpful acronym GEAR (generosity, equality, advocacy and responsibility) as a template for the work of justice Christians carry out in the world.

In week three, you did the painful yet necessary work of identifying the idols of your heart and industry that threaten your ability to pursue mercy and justice.

In week four, you were given the paradigm of the beloved community as a picture of embodied justice, and you were reminded of the need for proximity to those on the margins.

In week five, you were given a new lens through which to see your work and industry as God sees them, through a creation-fall-redemption paradigm. Each of these weeks came with a helpful case study to see these ideas actualized, as well as a concrete practice to implement. Look how far you have journeyed!

But there's just one problem. With the speed of the modern world, learning often becomes a rapid process of consuming information, completing the objectives and moving on to the next venture. This frenzied pace threatens to sabotage the progress you have made in this course. Therefore, instead of giving you new content for this final week together, this lesson focuses on cementing key insights and helping you to discern next steps, both individually and collectively.

The work of justice and mercy in your workplaces and industries will be a marathon, not a sprint. For many, it will involve a deliberate, ordinary faithfulness over a long period of time. It has been said, "We often overestimate what we can accomplish in a year but underestimate what can be done in ten years." Through the hidden work of prayer and the incredible power of the Holy Spirit, you might look back in a decade's time and marvel at all that God has done in your midst.

OBJECTIVES

- Clarify and reflect on the key concepts from this course.

- Identify individually and communally the next steps to take in your work and industries.

- Commission those in your group to embody this biblical integration of mercy and justice at work.

- Spend time in prayer for your workplaces, one another and for your great need of the Holy Spirit to discern your next steps.

Assignments

- Watch: *"Conclusion"* video with Lauren Gill.

- Practice: Identify an Accountability Partner.

(The video can be accessed by scanning the QR code or by visiting globalfaithandwork.com/missionaldisciplevideos.)

Conclusion

COMMUNITY DISCUSSION

The group discussion for this final week comprises two key sections. First, you will look back on the journey you have been on. Second, you will look forward to what God is inviting you into next.

1. LOOKING BACK

- As you look back on the past five weeks, what was the most important concept you have learned and why? How has it changed your paradigm of faith and work, or mercy and justice?

- As you look back on the past five weeks, recall some of the important insights that other group members shared. Spend some time encouraging one another in how the learning not only took place through the videos but through one another.

- What was a theme of this course that you would like to explore further?

- Where do you personally feel called to action? Have you spent time in prayer in this area?

2. LOOKING FORWARD

As you look forward, use the template below as a way to clarify what steps you will take over the following week, month, year and ten years. Allow 10–15 minutes of individual reflection time before gathering back together to discuss what you each wrote down.

WEEK	MONTH	YEAR	10 YEARS
Pray for God to reveal areas of injustice in your workplace. Pray for his clear direction around actions you should take through his power.	*Pray for all those in your workplace and industry. Pray especially for those with the least amount of power. Pray for God's clear direction around actions you should take.*	*Pray for God to give you vision for an area of brokenness in your industry, for which you can spend the next year praying for renewal. Pray for wisdom for how you can steward your power well.*	*Pray for God to use your industry, workplace and field to reflect more of God over the next decade. Pray for him to be glorified, as the work of your field becomes a place for those on the margins to be brought to the center.*
What one simple step could you take this week to see greater integration of justice and mercy in your workplace?	*As you look at your work calendar this next month, what could you intentionally shape as a restorative presence?*	*What area of brokenness in your industry or workplace is the Holy Spirit leading you to push against for renewal in the next year?*	*What would flourishing look like in your work/industry as justice and mercy take root? What stories would you tell of people and systems?*

WEEK	MONTH	YEAR	10 YEARS
Consider the four themes of beloved community as you reflect on your simple step: stewarding your power well, recognition and honor, listening with empathy and compassion, and conflict and forgiveness.	*Think through what practices, policies or people are affected by your work and how God may want to shape that.*	*Brainstorm ways you can steward your power for those who have less power in your field over the next year.*	*Craft a paragraph of what kind of things would be happening if this flourishing were to take place in your field. Then this year, start sharing this vision with coworkers of what could happen in your midst.*

FURTHER NOTES

PRACTICE: Identify an Accountability Partner

As we have already noted, the work of justice and mercy in your workplaces and industries is a marathon, not a sprint, and so it's essential to have people around you who can spur you on when you begin to tire. The practice this week is therefore to identify an individual who will hold you accountable to growing in a life of mercy and justice in your work. This might be someone who has journeyed with you in this course, or it may be an existing accountability partner. Agree with that person what accountability questions are helpful for them to ask you, and how often you will check in with him or her.

PRAYER PROMPTS

- Pray that God would allow the experiences and lessons learned during this six-week journey to bear fruit in your hearts and lives.

- Pray that God would use your work and workplaces to fulfill his vision of mercy and justice so that all people might flourish.

- Pray that God would help each person in your group to take their next faithful steps in embodying mercy and justice in and through their work.

CLOSING THOUGHTS

The story of Scripture begins with a garden but ends with a garden city. God's mission was not for people to return to the garden but for the garden to be cultivated into a city where everyone flourishes. Revelation 21 says:

> *Then I saw "a new heaven and a new earth," for the first heaven and the first earth had passed away, and there was no longer any sea. I saw the Holy City, the new Jerusalem, coming down out of heaven from God, prepared as a bride beautifully dressed for her husband. And I heard a loud voice from the throne saying, "Look! God's dwelling place is now among the people, and he will dwell with them. They will be his people, and God himself will be with them and be their God. 'He will wipe every tear from their eyes. There will be no more death' or mourning or crying or pain, for the old order of things has passed away."*

REVELATION 21:1–4

In this holy city, the nations will join together in unity yet not uniformity. They will co-reign as a "kingdom of priests" with Christ (Revelation 5:10). In this city, there will be no one on the margins but rather everyone will have a seat at the table with the King. In this city, power will be freely stewarded on behalf of others, and justice will be poured out on everyone who has been treated unfairly. In this city, story after story will be shared of God's redemptive work to rescue his good creation from sin and unleash women and men to live into their vocational callings.

In your workplace and industry, will you embody a foretaste of the holy city that is to come? Will you join in on God's desire to see missional disciples integrate mercy and justice at work? To close your time together as a group, commission one another with these words:

Commissioning

Identify a leader who will say the "unbolded" words, while the rest of the group will respond in **bold**. Have everyone reach out their hands as an act of receiving this commissioning.

INTRODUCTION

Leader:

O God, you have made us in your image to care for and cultivate your good creation. However, we recognize our work is filled with thorns and thistles, injustice and mistreatment.

The world is not the way it is supposed to be.

Yet, O God, you have not abandoned your world, but through Jesus Christ, seeds of new creation sprout forth everywhere we look.

O Spirit, breath of the living God, would you send us now as partners with Christ into every industry to demonstrate and declare good news until Christ's return.

Group: **Set us apart, Lord, we are listening.**

FEET

Leader:

O Christ, may our feet be commissioned by your washing to walk as faithful servants into areas of brokenness and pain.

Group: **Lord, tend to the soil of our hearts.**

EYES

Leader:

O Christ, may our eyes be set on the plight of those on the margins.

Group: **Lord, tend to the soil of our hearts.**

EARS

Leader:

O Christ, may our ears be opened to the cries of the overlooked and mistreated.

Group: **Lord, tend to the soil of our hearts.**

MOUTHS

Leader:

O Christ, may our mouths be loosened to speak on behalf of the quieted and dismissed.

Group: **Lord, tend to the soil of our hearts.**

HANDS

Leader:

O Christ, may our hands be extended to repair what's broken and restore what's been left in disarray.

Group: **Lord, tend to the soil of our hearts.**

CLOSING

Group:

God the Father,

call your lost creation back home.

God, the Son,

act on behalf of the weak, the poor and the powerless.

God, the Spirit,

give us a glimpse and taste of the kingdom through our work, now and forevermore.

Amen.

Notes

Contributors

1. Abe Cho

Contributor

Abe is the senior director of training with Redeemer City to City New York City and North America. He has more than 20 years of urban pastoral ministry experience, with a particular emphasis on forming disciples for both faith and work and mercy and justice. He served for 14 years as a pastor at Redeemer Presbyterian Church in New York City, with six of those years as the senior pastor of Redeemer Presbyterian Church East Side. Abe holds an MDiv from Gordon-Conwell Theological Seminary and a DMin from Fuller Theological Seminary. He and his wife, Jordyn, have four children and live in Manhattan.

2. Kimberly Deckel

Author

Kimberly serves as executive pastor at Church of the Cross in Austin, Texas. In addition to her vocation as a priest, Kimberly has extensive experience as a clinical social worker, as well as in organizational leadership. Kimberly also serves as the director of Faith, Work, Mercy, and Justice for City to City North America.

3. Lauren Gill

General Editor and Author

Lauren is the director of the Global Faith & Work Initiative at Redeemer City to City, where she works with pastors, church planters and ministry leaders around the world to equip their lay leaders to push against brokenness in every industry and field. Prior to working for Redeemer City to City, she worked with the Center for Faith & Work and has been in the faith and work sphere since 2009. She holds an MA in Counseling Psychology from Columbia University and a BFA in Drama and Journalism from New York University. She lives in New York City with her husband, Suneel, and their two children.

4. Robert Guerrero

Contributor

Robert is a Redeemer City to City vice president and director of the Latino Initiative of City to City North America. He works toward catalyzing church planting networks in key cities of North America and the Hispanic Caribbean.

Born to Dominican parents in New York City, Robert has spent much of his life in both the US and Dominican Republic. He has planted churches in Santo Domingo (Dominican Republic), Chicago and New York City. Robert was also cofounder of La Red del Camino for Integral Mission in Latin America, a movement committed to inspiring and training churches to live out the gospel holistically with a commitment to justice, compassion and community renewal. He now lives in Miami, from where he leads the recently launched Latino Initiative of City to City North America. Robert and his wife, Damaris, have four sons: Joshua, Tomas, Robert Jr. and Joel.

5. Charlie Meo

Author

Charlie serves as a pastor of Missio Dei Communities in Tempe, Arizona and contributes to the direction and shaping of curriculum within the Surge Network, a movement of local churches seeking to put Jesus on display by equipping, reconciling and activating God's people in Arizona. He and his wife, Keaton, are together raising three children: Clarke, Cosette and Henri.

6. Dennae Pierre

Author

Dennae lives in downtown Phoenix, Arizona and is co-director for City to City North America, The Crete Collective and the Surge Network. She has been involved in church planting, community development and immigration reform, and she also started a non-profit that serves birth mothers whose children are in the foster care system. She holds an MA from Covenant Theological Seminary and a DMin from Western Theological Seminary and is the author of *Healing Prayers & Meditations to Resist a Violent World*. Dennae is married to Vermon, the lead pastor of Roosevelt Community Church, and they have five children: Marcel, Mya, Judah, Jovanna and Rosa Joy.

7. Susan Nacorda Stang

Contributor

Susan serves as groups pastor at Fellowship Monrovia, a gospel-centered, multiethnic, intergenerational church in Los Angeles. She was previously the director of Leadership Development at Redeemer Downtown and Redeemer Presbyterian Church in New York City, where she worked for over 13 years. She also served on staff with the Navigators at her alma mater, New York University. Susan is married to Kyle, and they live in Southern California with their two wonderful daughters, Isabelle and Elise.

8. Missy Wallace

Author

Missy is managing director of Redeemer City to City and its Global Faith & Work Initiative. Missy is the founder of the Nashville Institute for Faith and Work (NIFW), where she previously worked as executive director. Earlier in her career, Missy worked for more than a decade at Bank of America in Charlotte, NC; The Boston Consulting Group in Chicago, Singapore and Bangkok; and Time Warner in New York City.

Missy has published articles for The Gospel Coalition and Common Good and has spoken at faith and work conferences around the world. Missy holds a BA in economics from Vanderbilt University and an MBA from the Kellogg Graduate School of Management at Northwestern. She and her husband, Paul, have three adult children.

Notes

REDEEMER
CITY to CITY

Redeemer City to City (CTC) is a non-profit organization that prayerfully recruits, trains, coaches and resources leaders who cultivate gospel movements in global cities primarily through church planting. CTC is based in New York City and works in over 75 global cities throughout Africa, Asia, Australia, North America, Latin America, the Middle East and Europe. CTC's core competencies are urban church planting, leadership development and content creation. All of this is done to help bring the gospel of Jesus Christ to cities.

For more information about Redeemer City to City, please visit **redeemercitytocity.com**.

GLOBAL
FAITH & WORK
INITIATIVE
A MINISTRY OF REDEEMER CITY TO CITY

The Global Faith & Work Initiative (GFWI) is a ministry of Redeemer City to City. GFWI equips, connects, and mobilizes churches and city networks around the world for gospel-centered faith and work ministry with consulting, resources and training.

If you enjoyed the material in *The Missional Disciple*, please visit **globalfaithandwork.com** for more resources to integrate your faith and work and to sign up for our newsletter.